THE · WORLD · AROUND · US
THE SEA

BRIAN WILLIAMS

Illustrated by
Graham Allen, Mike Atkinson, Chris Forsey
Ron Jobson, Cliff Meadway, Francis Phillips, Doug Post
Nina Roberts, Mike Saunders, Charlotte Snook
Bill Stallion

Kingfisher Books

Series design: Pinpoint Design Co.
Cover design: Terry Woodley
Cover illustration: Mick Loates/Linden Artists

Kingfisher Books, Grisewood & Dempsey Ltd,
Elsley House, 24–30 Great Titchfield Street, London W1P 7AD.
This edition first published in 1991 by Kingfisher Books.
Material in this edition was previously published in 1979,
under the title *Secrets of The Sea*.

10 9 8 7 6 5 4 3 2 1

British Library Cataloguing in Publication Data
Williams, Brian 1943–
    The sea
    1. Oceans
    I. Title II. Series
    551.46
ISBN 0 86272 821 5

Phototypeset by Southern Positives and Negatives (SPAN),
Lingfield, Surrey.
Printed in Spain.

Contents

The Birth of the Oceans 4
The Watery World 6
The Restless Sea 8
The Living Sea 10
A Design for Life 12
The Seashore 14
The Coral Seas 16
Whales and Dolphins 18
The Darkest Depths 20
Ocean Oddities 22
Hunters and Hunted 24
The Wanderers 26

Dangers of the Deep 28
Diving 30
Exploring the Depths 32
Underwater Farming 34
Wealth from the Sea 36
New Technology 38
Living Under the Sea 40
Submarines 42
Monsters and Mysteries 44
Sunken Treasure 46
Useful Words 47
Index 48

The Birth of the Oceans

100 million years ago

Many millions of years ago, the areas of land and sea on the Earth looked very different.

350 million years ago

These two maps show how the land areas have gradually moved and changed.

The Earth is about 4600 million years old, but its oceans are much younger. Some scientists think the Earth was formed from dust and gas particles floating around the Sun. Over millions of years gravity pulled the particles together, forming the Earth's core.

In the Beginning

As the particles came together, gases were released and created the Earth's atmosphere. Slowly the surface of the Earth cooled and steam and clouds appeared in the atmosphere. The Earth probably looked like the planet Venus does today – a lifeless, rocky desert, covered in poisonous clouds.

Scientists think the water that created the oceans either fell as rain, formed from the steam and clouds in the atmosphere, or was released from the Earth's rocks as they cooled. Over hundreds of years the water collected in the low areas of land. These gradually filled up and joined together to become the first oceans.

Life on Earth

The land was too harsh and barren to support life, but the oceans were a kinder environment. Slowly, the oceans became a kind of chemical 'soup', in which the first living things appeared – simple plant-like organisms, which quickly spread through the oceans. But it was not until millions of years later that the first simple animals appeared.

The Watery World

Almost three-quarters of the Earth's surface is covered by sea. Beneath the water there are mountains, valleys and plains, as there are on dry land. Around the edges of the great continents runs a sloping underwater platform called the continental shelf. The shallow water on this shelf is rich in plant and animal life.

The ocean floor, or oceanic crust, is made up of a series of curved plates, constantly grinding together to form ridges and trenches. The deepest parts of the sea lie in the Pacific Ocean. Here the crust disappears into trenches delving deep into the Earth's interior. Because of all this movement, the oldest rocks found on the seabed are only 200 million years old – much younger than rocks found on land.

The most common chemical in the sea is salt. Both the temperature and the salt content of the sea affect its density. Because of this, ships carry the Plimsoll line marks shown above, which indicate how different densities affect the limits to which a ship may be loaded.

▶ Icebergs contain hardly any salt, they could be towed by tugs to areas where fresh water is scarce. The saltiest part of the iceberg is at the bottom. So, as the iceberg melts, fresh water (being less dense) floats on top of the sea and can be pumped off into storage tanks.

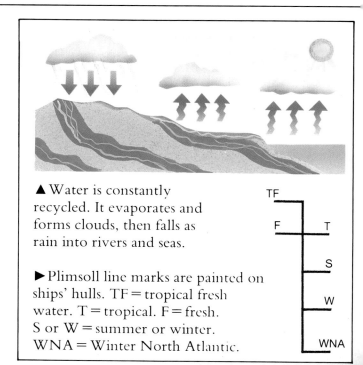

▲ Water is constantly recycled. It evaporates and forms clouds, then falls as rain into rivers and seas.

▶ Plimsoll line marks are painted on ships' hulls. TF = tropical fresh water. T = tropical. F = fresh. S or W = summer or winter. WNA = Winter North Atlantic.

Only about one ninth of an iceberg is ever visible above the sea's surface.

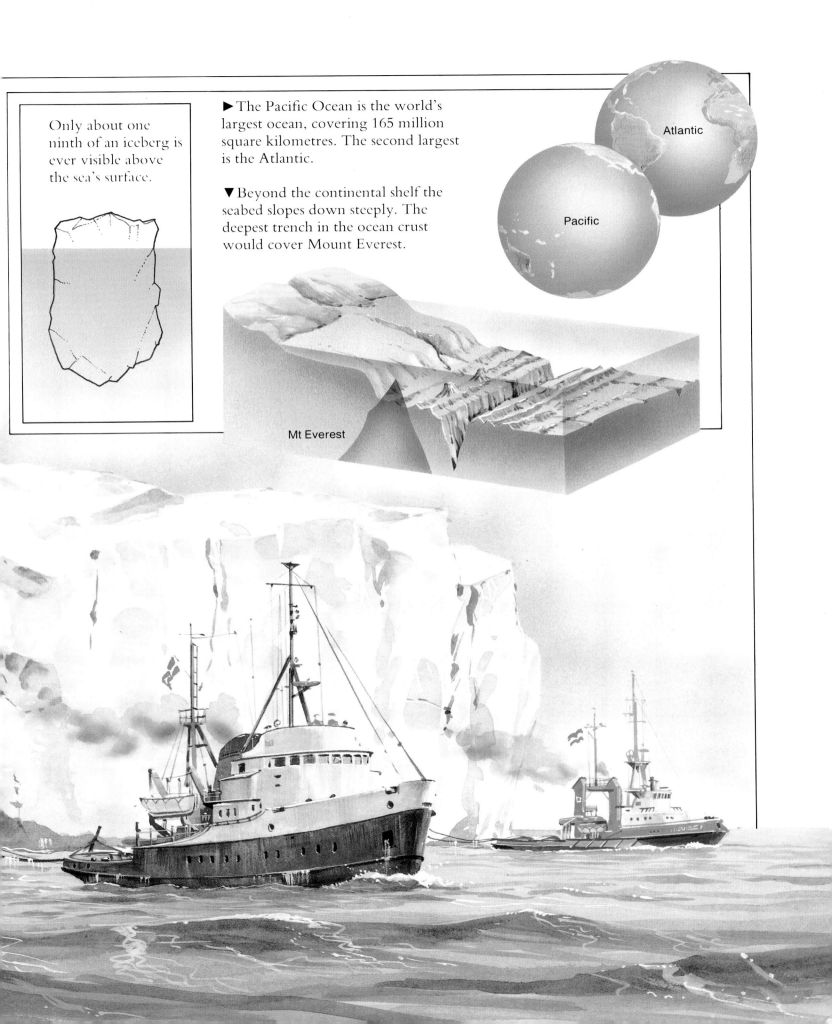

►The Pacific Ocean is the world's largest ocean, covering 165 million square kilometres. The second largest is the Atlantic.

▼Beyond the continental shelf the seabed slopes down steeply. The deepest trench in the ocean crust would cover Mount Everest.

Atlantic

Pacific

Mt Everest

The Restless Sea

The waters of the world's seas and oceans are always moving, stirred by the winds, waves, tides and currents.

The tides are caused by the Moon's gravity tugging at the Earth and its seas. Every 24 hours there are two high tides and two low tides. Occasionally, the Sun's gravitational pull joins with that of the Moon, and when this happens there is a much higher tide, called a spring or rising tide.

Waves and Currents

Every wave is made up of tiny water particles moving in a circle. The wind pushes the wave upwards, and then gravity pulls it down again. Watch a bird floating on the water. The waves seem to roll right under it, while the bird remains in the same spot.

Ocean currents are bodies of water that always flow in the same direction. North of the Equator, the currents of the Atlantic and Pacific oceans move in huge, clockwise circles. South of the Equator, the currents move in an anti-clockwise direction.

▶ In the Bay of Fundy in Canada, the tide rises 15 metres. The fish are left stranded on walls of nets.

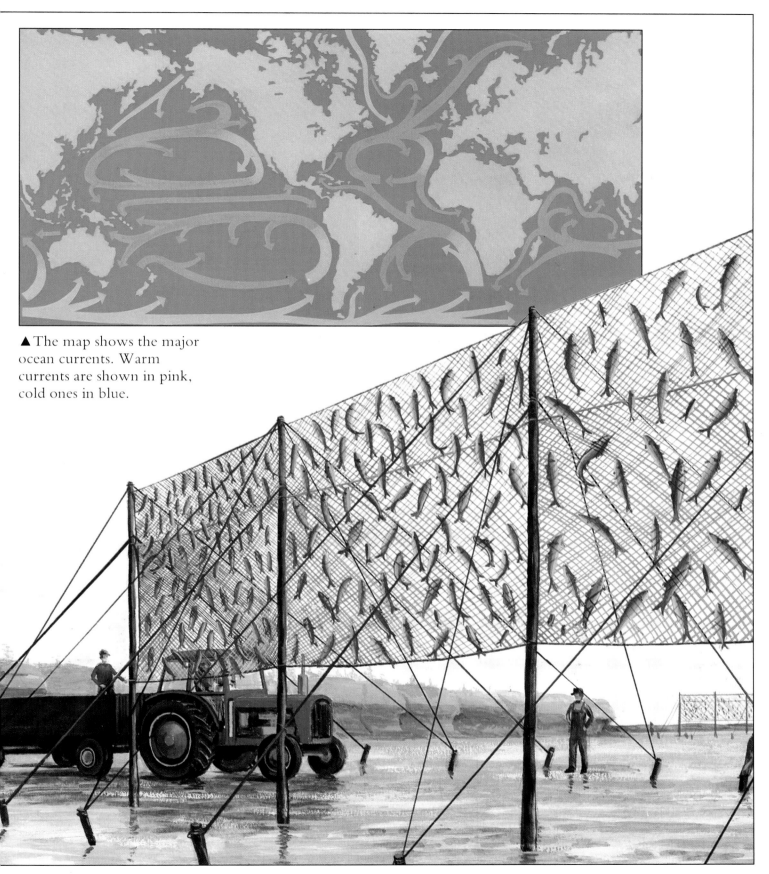

▲ The map shows the major ocean currents. Warm currents are shown in pink, cold ones in blue.

The Living Sea

Life in the sea is ruled by three forces – the Sun, water pressure (the weight of water pressing down from above) and food.

Sunlight is made up of many colours, as is shown by a rainbow. Each colour can only travel to a certain depth in sea water. As the diagram opposite shows, red light fades out first and violet light travels deepest.

Hot and Cold

Sunlight warms the oceans and the warm water forms a thin layer at the surface of the sea. Beneath this layer is a band of water where the temperature falls sharply. The cold water below this is rich in food.

The most fertile areas of the sea are those where the barrier between hot and cold water is easily broken, by big waves for example. This allows the animals and plants in the warm water to feed on the food-rich cold water that has broken through.

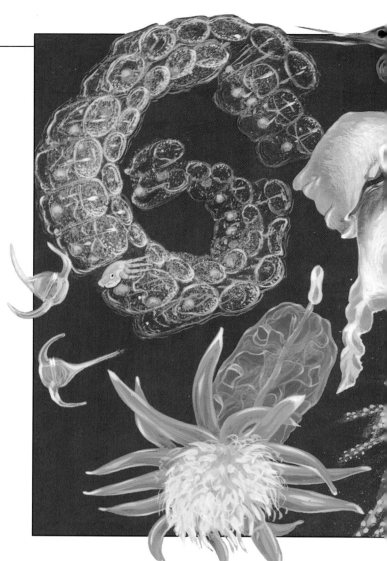

Cleaner

Barracuda

False cleaner

◄ Most sea creatures depend on others in some way. The fierce barracuda lets a cleaner fish feed on food scraps in its jaws, and so cleans its teeth. The false cleaner looks like the real one and so avoids attack, but it does not do the same useful task.

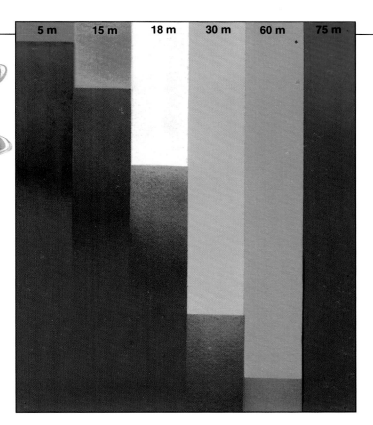

▲ The depths to which the different colours in light will travel through sea water.

| 5 m | 15 m | 18 m | 30 m | 60 m | 75 m |

The Ocean Larder

Among the most important life forms in the sea are the tiny plants called phytoplankton. These make their food using sunlight, as land plants do. The plants also enrich the sea with oxygen and provide food for tiny animals, called zooplankton. Examples of plant and animal plankton are shown on the left, magnified many times, as they would appear through a microscope.

Many kinds of fish, whales, seals, squid and shellfish depend on plankton for food. Some of these animals, in turn, provide food for other sea creatures, such as sharks. So all ocean creatures ultimately depend on plankton for their survival.

The wake of a ship or a swimming bird stirs up the surface of the sea. At night the broken water may glow with light – you can sometimes see it when a wave crashes on the shore. This strange light is produced by tiny plankton, which are active at night.

A Design for Life

Fish were the first vertebrate, or backboned, animals. They are adapted in many ways to their watery environment. Most have a gas-filled air bladder rather like a balloon inside their bodies to keep them afloat. The amount of gas in the bladder adjusts to whatever depth the fish is at, so that the fish remains buoyant. Sharks do not have swim bladders and must keep moving about all the time, otherwise they would sink.

Fish have good senses of sight, taste, hearing and smell. Some make noises, by grating their teeth or vibrating their swim bladders, for communication or defence.

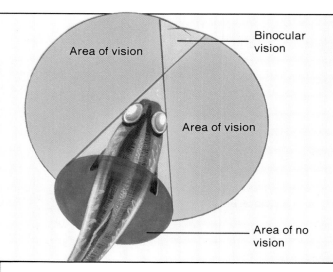

Area of vision

Binocular vision

Area of vision

Area of no vision

Sunfish

Movement of a swimming fish

◄The ocean sunfish was once thought to lie flat on the surface, basking in the sun – hence its name. A sunfish can be 3 metres long and weigh up to a tonne.

EYESIGHT
Eyesight is a key sense in most species. A fish's eyes, which bulge out from either side of its head, give it a wide field of vision on each side. Instead of clear-cut objects, a fish sees movements, which alert it to danger. With some fish the fields of vision for each eye overlap at the front. This gives the fish the advantage of binocular vision, which means that it can focus both eyes on one object at the same time, as we do. This helps it to judge distance when seizing prey. But it can only do this when its prey is directly in front of it.

MOVEMENT
Most fish swim with powerful side-to-side strokes of their tails which push the water aside. The pectoral and pelvic fins are mainly used for steering and balance. The dorsal fin is used as a rudder. When swimming at speed the fins sometimes fold flat against the body. Fish have an acute sense of temperature and can tell, to a fraction of a degree, the instant they swim into warmer water.

◄The goby uses its fan-shaped pectoral fins for clinging to rocks. The first land animals were fish, who used their fins in this way until the fins slowly developed into limbs.

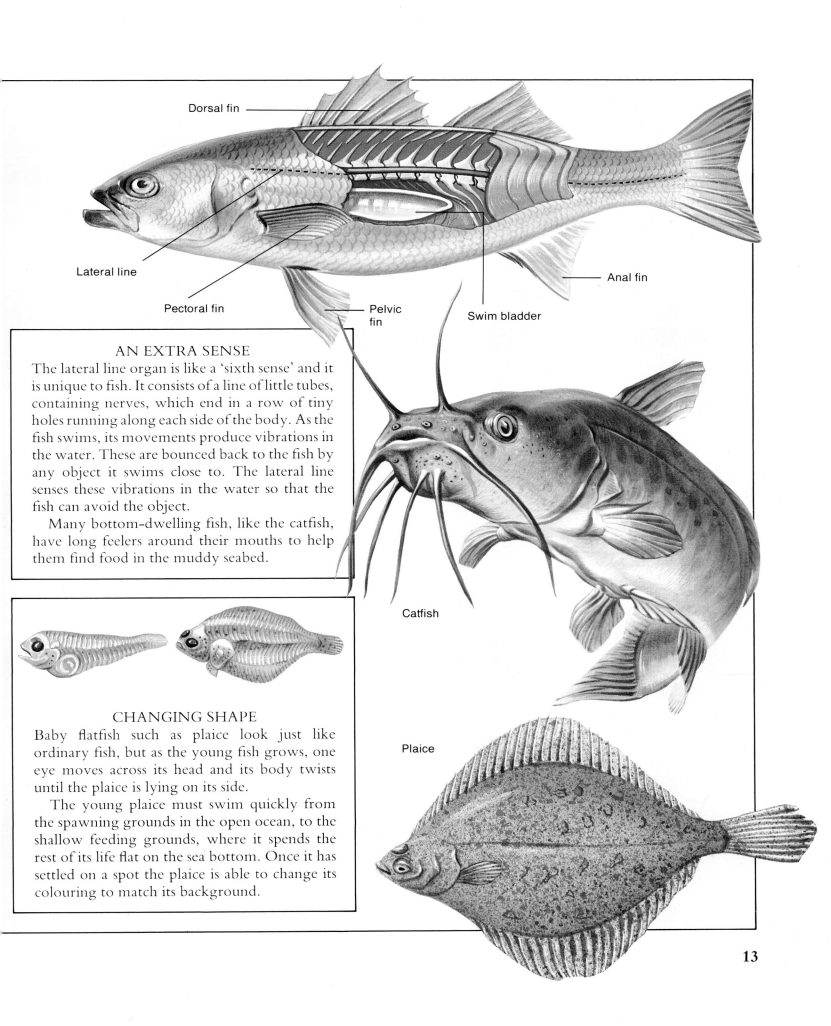

Dorsal fin

Lateral line

Pectoral fin

Pelvic fin

Anal fin

Swim bladder

AN EXTRA SENSE

The lateral line organ is like a 'sixth sense' and it is unique to fish. It consists of a line of little tubes, containing nerves, which end in a row of tiny holes running along each side of the body. As the fish swims, its movements produce vibrations in the water. These are bounced back to the fish by any object it swims close to. The lateral line senses these vibrations in the water so that the fish can avoid the object.

Many bottom-dwelling fish, like the catfish, have long feelers around their mouths to help them find food in the muddy seabed.

Catfish

CHANGING SHAPE

Baby flatfish such as plaice look just like ordinary fish, but as the young fish grows, one eye moves across its head and its body twists until the plaice is lying on its side.

The young plaice must swim quickly from the spawning grounds in the open ocean, to the shallow feeding grounds, where it spends the rest of its life flat on the sea bottom. Once it has settled on a spot the plaice is able to change its colouring to match its background.

Plaice

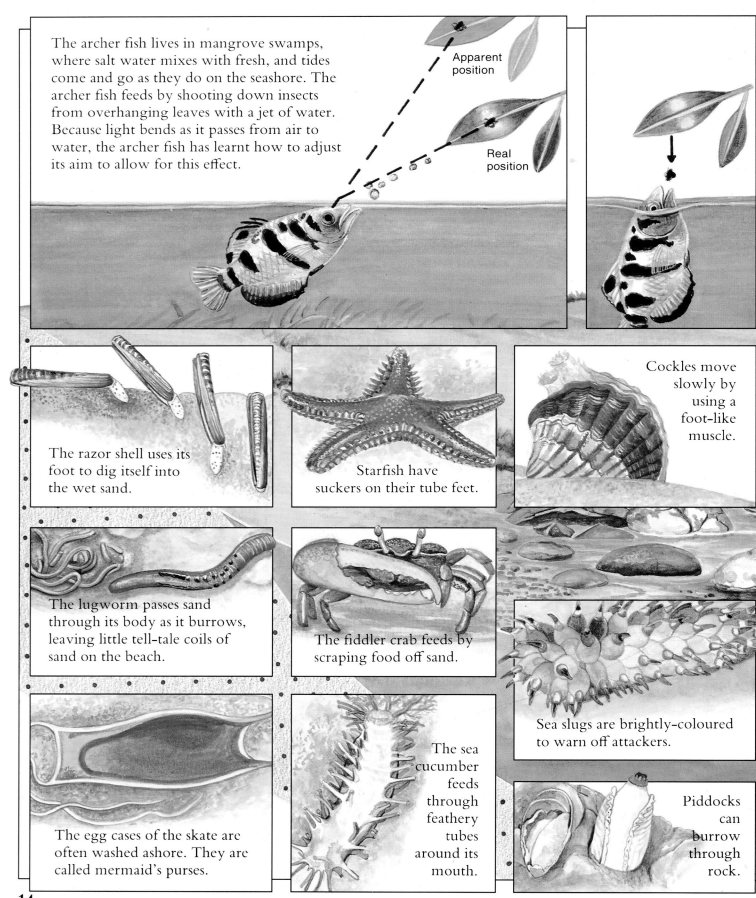

The archer fish lives in mangrove swamps, where salt water mixes with fresh, and tides come and go as they do on the seashore. The archer fish feeds by shooting down insects from overhanging leaves with a jet of water. Because light bends as it passes from air to water, the archer fish has learnt how to adjust its aim to allow for this effect.

Apparent position

Real position

The razor shell uses its foot to dig itself into the wet sand.

Starfish have suckers on their tube feet.

Cockles move slowly by using a foot-like muscle.

The lugworm passes sand through its body as it burrows, leaving little tell-tale coils of sand on the beach.

The fiddler crab feeds by scraping food off sand.

Sea slugs are brightly-coloured to warn off attackers.

The egg cases of the skate are often washed ashore. They are called mermaid's purses.

The sea cucumber feeds through feathery tubes around its mouth.

Piddocks can burrow through rock.

14

The Seashore

In the open sea conditions do not change much, but the seashore changes every day, as the tide rises and falls. It is sometimes wet and sometimes dry. It can be warmed by the Sun or chilled by wind and rain.

Every animal and plant of the seashore is used to these conditions. Many are able to live partly in water and partly in air.

Some seaweeds are found inshore, clinging to rocks when the tide is out. Creatures such as limpets and barnacles live on rocks, too. Their hard shells protect them when the tide is out. Other animals find shelter by burying themselves in wet sand, while rock pools harbour all types of small sea creatures, such as starfish, crabs and sea anemones.

The mudskipper uses its fins to crawl over the mud.

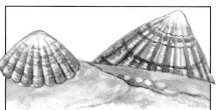

Limpets clamp onto rocks when the tide is out.

At low tide periwinkles shelter beneath seaweed, or glue themselves to rocks.

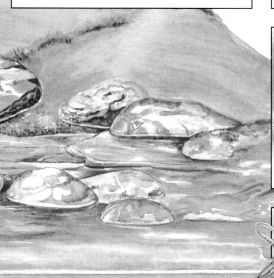

A sea mouse burrows in sand to hide the bright colours on its bristles.

Sand eels feed on the eggs of many small seashore creatures. They will sometimes bury themselves in the sand when the tide goes out.

Cuttlefish live out at sea, but sometimes their white shells are washed ashore.

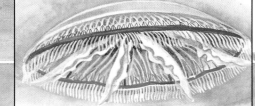

Jellyfish are also often washed ashore with the tide.

The various creatures that live along the seashore have all found ways of dealing with the difficult conditions there. On sandy beaches, some shellfish seek shelter by burrowing into damp sand. In this way they stop their bodies drying out, and at the same time are protected from the force of incoming waves. When the tide is in, shellfish, such as cockles and razor shells, feed by thrusting up siphon tubes with which they filter tiny bits of food from the water.

The Coral Seas

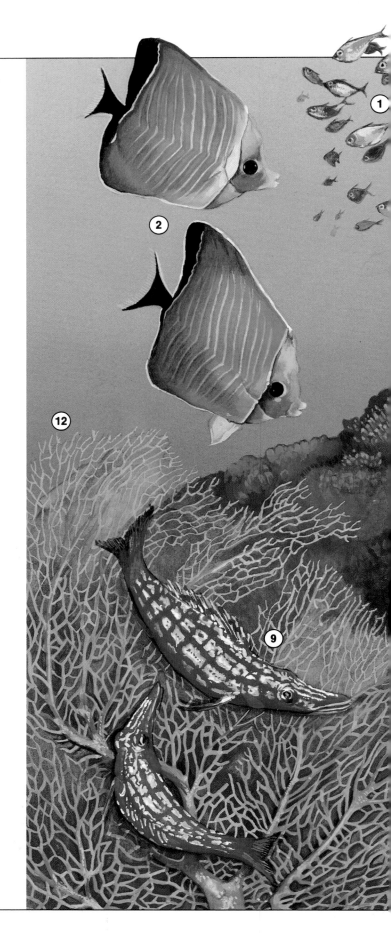

A coral reef is an undersea garden made out of limestone. It is built by tiny animals called polyps. Polyps begin life as floating larvae before settling on the seabed. Once settled, the polyps grow a hard chalky skeleton to support them and the new growths that 'bud' from the parent. Polyp colonies can grow to include thousands of polyps, all sharing a common skeleton.

Friends and Enemies

Coral grows only in warm shallow water, where sunlight can reach it. This is because the polyps live in partnership with tiny plankton plants that need sunlight to survive. The plants supply the coral with oxygen.

Coral polyps feed by putting out tentacles to catch tiny creatures floating past. The coral's chief enemy is the crown of thorns starfish, which feeds on live polyps, leaving behind only the white, brittle skeleton.

A Garden Home

The water flowing over the reef carries with it a rich food supply, and this, along with the shelter the reef provides, attracts many sea animals. The fish are often brightly coloured to match the coral. This makes it difficult for enemies, such as the grouper, to spot them.

Some fish act as gardeners, pruning the tips of the coral. Others, such as the squirrel fish, hide in the cracks and crevices of the coral during the day and come out to feed at night. The parrot fish feeds on reef algae and at night hides itself in a covering of slime.

A coral reef is home to a great variety of different fish and other sea animals. Some are attracted by the protection the coral offers, others by the food they find there.

(1) Gaterins
(2) Butterfly fish
(3) Lion fish
(4) Parrot fish
(5) Squirrel fish
(6) Staghorn coral
(7) Soft coral
(8) Coral trout
(9) Hawk fish
(10) Sea anemone
(11) Crown of thorns starfish
(12) Fan coral
(13) Grouper

Whales and Dolphins

Whales are the largest and most intelligent animals in the sea. They are not fish, but belong to a group of animals known as mammals, which includes most large land animals as well as humans.

There are two main types of whale. The toothed whales (which include porpoises and dolphins) and the baleen whales. Toothed whales catch squid and small fish. Baleen whales eat only the tiny shrimp-like krill (a form of plankton), which they strain from the water with their sieve-like mouths.

A Breath of Fresh Air

Like all mammals, a whale has to breathe air, it cannot breathe underwater. Before diving, the whale takes in a deep breath. It can remain submerged for up to two hours.

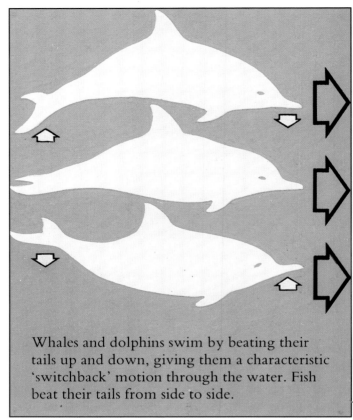

Whales and dolphins swim by beating their tails up and down, giving them a characteristic 'switchback' motion through the water. Fish beat their tails from side to side.

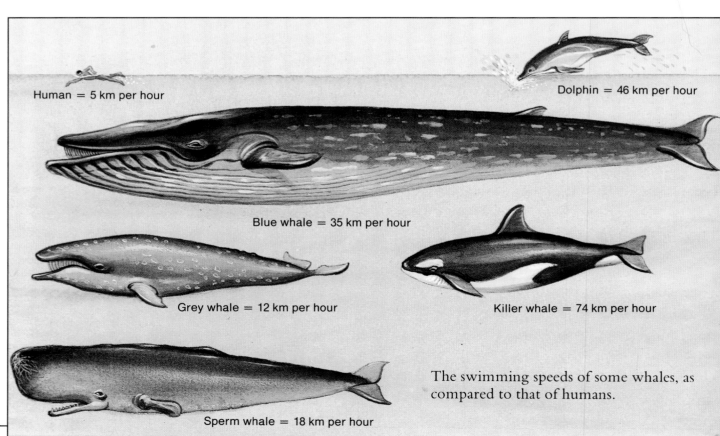

Human = 5 km per hour

Dolphin = 46 km per hour

Blue whale = 35 km per hour

Grey whale = 12 km per hour

Killer whale = 74 km per hour

Sperm whale = 18 km per hour

The swimming speeds of some whales, as compared to that of humans.

◄The dolphin needs to breathe every 30 seconds or so. The killer whale (below) may stay submerged for up to two hours. On surfacing, it spouts out a spray of water vapour and used air.

Because whales are mammals, they give birth to live young. A baby whale is born tail first and is pushed to the surface by its mother for its first breath of air.

Whales communicate with each other by means of clicks, whistles and grunts.

Under Threat

People and sharks are the most dangerous enemies to the whale. Whales have been hunted for their oil and meat for centuries. Today, several species of whale (including the largest animal on Earth, the giant blue) are close to dying out altogether. Even so, some dolphins and whales are still hunted.

The beluga whale can send and receive messages in the form of sound waves. These tell it the speed and size of nearby creatures.

The Darkest Depths

The deep-sea world is a cold and almost totally dark place. Although many of the fish that live there look fierce, most are less than 10 centimetres long and have very poor eyesight. Some are even blind.

The only light in this black world comes from some of the creatures themselves. These animals have chemicals in their bodies that make parts of them glow with light. The fish use their lights to attract a mate or to confuse attackers. Some of these deep-sea creatures are able to produce an impressive display of flashing lights if attacked.

Fishing in the Dark

Other fish, such as the angler fish, use their lights as lures, to attract passing victims within reach of their jaws. The angler fish has also evolved a strange way of finding a mate. The tiny male attaches himself to the much larger female and becomes part of her body.

Deep-sea fish can withstand the enormous pressure in deep water. Some can even adapt to pressure differences, and at night these fish hunt for food closer to the surface, where the pressure is not so great.

(1) Deep sea squid.
(2) The angler fish has lights on both its upper and lower jaws.
(3) *Eustomias filifera* has an elaborate lure.
(4) The hatchet fish has huge eyes.
(5) *Pachystomias* uses its glowing cheek lights as headlamps.
(6) *Vinciguerrias* has a row of shining dots along its body.
(7) The viperfish has huge jaws and teeth.

Ocean Oddities

There are many strangely-shaped creatures living in the sea. One of these is the manta ray. It is sometimes called the 'devil fish', but in fact it is perfectly harmless, although the sting and electric rays are not so gentle.

Less harmless is the hagfish. This eel-like animal has teeth on its tongue, and a powerful sucking mouth. It attaches itself to the side of a dead or dying fish and scrapes away at the skin, eating the flesh and sucking the blood.

▶ The marine iguana of the Galapagos Islands is the only seagoing lizard. It can stay under water for up to an hour.

▲ The manta ray has broad fins, shaped like wings, which can be up to 7 metres across from tip to tip. It uses its fins to 'fly' through the water. Manta rays are strong swimmers, and these inquisitive and gentle giants have been known to allow divers to hitch a ride. It uses its 'horns' as fans to guide plankton into its mouth.

▶ The sea slug is related to the land slug. It usually relies on its colour to put off any animal that might want to eat it.

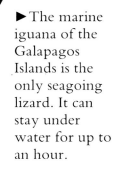

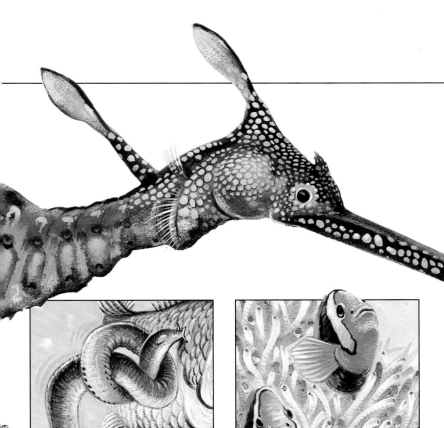

◄In spite of its name, the sea dragon is far from fierce. Its body is covered with leaflike growths that camouflage it to look like a piece of seaweed. Another name for the sea dragon is the Australian seahorse.

Spiders and Slugs

Some of the most interesting oddities are the smaller creatures, such as the sea spider and the sea slug. The sea spider is not a true spider, although it does have eight legs. Its stomach extends down into its legs because its body is so tiny.

The little sea slug is very brightly coloured, which is thought to be a means of defence. Sea slugs feed on sea anemones, covering the anemone's poisonous spines with slime to make them harmless. The slugs may also stick a dead anemone's stinging cells to their own bodies as an extra means of defence.

Sea Snakes

Sea snakes, like many land snakes, kill their victims with poison. The strength of the venom varies with each type of snake, but as a rule, sea snakes that live in rougher seas have a stronger poison.

▲The hagfish (top) lives near the bottom of the sea. It feeds on the bodies of dead or dying fish until they are reduced to skeletons. Sea snakes (above) evolved, or developed, from land snakes that returned to the ocean. They swim well, but because they have to breathe air they can drown.

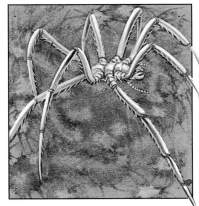

▲The damsel fish (top) lives in partnership with a sea anemone. The fish's slimy scales give it some protection against the anemone's stings, but still the damsel must 'court' its anemone before taking shelter in its tentacles. The sea spider (above) feeds on coral and other small sea animals.

Hunters and Hunted

In the struggle for food and for survival, both the hunters and the hunted of the sea have developed some startling adaptations, for attack and for defence.

Flying fish escape from hungry predators, such as albacore, by leaping out of the water and gliding through the air. Using their stiffened fins as wings they can stay airborne for nearly a minute.

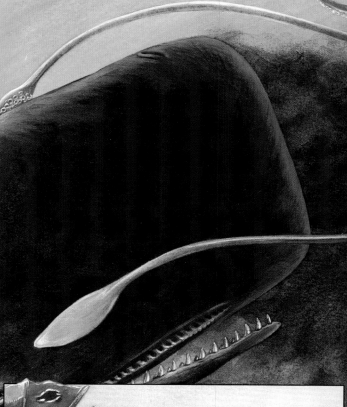

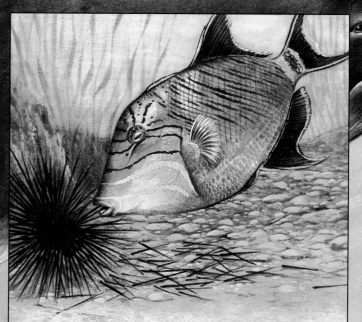

The trigger fish overturns a spiny sea urchin with a jet of water from its mouth, then eats the less spiny underside.

The dorsal fin of the decoy fish looks like a small fish. This lures others towards the waiting jaws of the real fish.

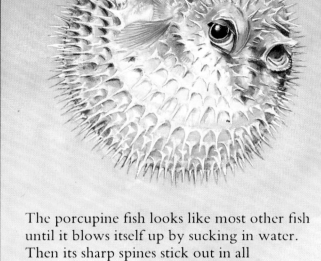

A BATTLE OF GIANTS

As a means of defence, squid are able to release an inky fluid to confuse their enemies. Sperm whales are the natural enemies of giant squid, and fierce battles sometimes take place in the depths. Some sperm whales have been found with long scars on their heads caused by the suckers on the squid's tentacles.

The porcupine fish looks like most other fish until it blows itself up by sucking in water. Then its sharp spines stick out in all directions, making it dangerous to eat. It has been claimed that the spines are sharp enough for the fish to cut its way out of a shark's stomach.

Pilot fish often swim close to sharks. They feed on scraps that are leftover after the sharks have made a kill.

A starfish can find a scallop by its smell and dig it out of the sand. The starfish then forces the two halves of the shell apart.

The Wanderers

Ocean migration is one of the marvels of nature. Although we know that some sea animals migrate to breed, we don't know how they find their way across vast areas of sea, to the same breeding grounds every year.

Guided by Instinct

Animals may know when to migrate because of seasonal changes in the water temperature, or small changes in the chemical balance of the sea, but it is instinct that tells them where to go. Smell may play a part too, for we know that salmon are guided back towards their home rivers by the smell of the estuary water.

Many animals migrate thousands of kilometres to reach their breeding grounds. Fur seals breed on rocky islands near Alaska, and some travel right across the Pacific Ocean from Japan to get

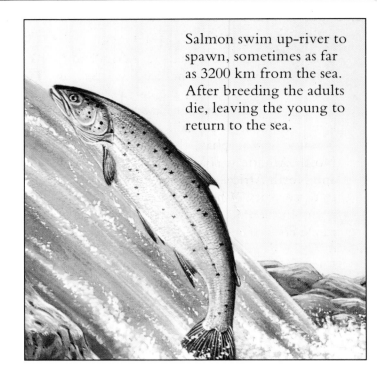

Salmon swim up-river to spawn, sometimes as far as 3200 km from the sea. After breeding the adults die, leaving the young to return to the sea.

there. Eels, too, travel vast distances. From the rivers of Europe, Africa and North America to the middle of the Atlantic Ocean.

These spiny crayfish form long columns, which wind across the seabed to their spawning grounds. The young animals that hatch from the eggs the crayfish lay are tiny, transparent versions of the adults.

ONCE IN A LIFETIME

Every year, eels from Europe, Africa and North America migrate to the Sargasso Sea in the Atlantic Ocean. There, the eels breed and then die. The eggs they produce hatch into transparent larvae, called leptocephali.

Some leptocephali then swim west to the North American coast, others head for Europe and North Africa – a journey which may take up to three years. When they get to the mouth of a river, the leptocephali change into young eels, called elvers. The elvers swim up-river in search of a lake or pond. There they will live and grow for eight to ten years before returning to the Sargasso Sea to breed.

Sargasso Sea

Leptocephalus

Eel

◀Northern fur seals collect on breeding beaches in the spring. The huge male seals, called bulls, fight each other to win territories and 'harems' of several females with which they can breed.

Dangers of the Deep

Hammerhead shark

Portuguese men-of-war

Scorpion fish

The sea is a dangerous place for those who are unfamiliar with it. Most sailors and divers fear sharks, although many are usually harmless to people. Among the dangerous sharks is the great white, or maneater, which can reach a length of about 11 metres. Other sharks that are known to attack people are the tiger shark, the great blue shark and the odd-looking hammerhead.

Hidden Dangers

Few ocean hunters will deliberately attack people. The moray eel lurks in rock crevices and will usually prefer to retreat, although an unwary diver risks losing a hand if the eel is disturbed.

A diver would be even more unlucky to be trapped in the jaws of a giant clam. The clam's shells snap tightly shut as an instant defence reaction against any would-be intruders.

The jaws of the great white shark are so strong they can dent the steel bars of a shark-proof cage.

Giant clam

Sea urchin

Moray eel

Poisoners of the Sea

Spiny sea urchins look like harmless plants, but their sharp, brittle spines often break off easily and can inflict a painful injury. Some sea urchins also have poisonous tips on their spines.

The Portuguese man-of-war is a poisonous jellyfish. Its tentacles can be 10 metres long, with stinging cells that contain venom more deadly than that of many snakes. Equally as poisonous is the spiny, but colourful scorpion fish.

Diving

People have been diving since ancient times, usually for pearls, shells and sponges. Early divers had to hold their breath and couldn't stay under for long. So people invented ways of breathing underwater.

Early Experiments

The earliest diving machines, called diving bells, simply trapped a pocket of air underwater, which the diver could use. One of the first diving suits was designed in 1797, It had a metal helmet, connected to hoses through which air was pumped, but if the diver bent forwards the air escaped and the helmet flooded. The Siebe diving suit of 1837 was safer. The diver was covered from head to toe so that no water could get in. Then, in 1855, two divers invented a suit with a small air tank on the back. This freed the diver from his air hose, but only for a few minutes.

Finally, in 1943, two Frenchmen developed the first 'aqualung', or self-contained underwater breathing apparatus – 'scuba' for short. At last divers were free of clumsy suits and air hoses. This gave them greater flexibility and avoided the danger of getting air hoses caught or damaged.

The Dangers of Diving

The air a diver breathes contains a large amount of nitrogen, which usually dissolves in the blood. As a diver goes deeper, the pressure

▼ Halley's diving bell of 1716, was supplied with air from weighted barrels lowered on a rope.

▼ The Klingert suit of 1797, had many features that later became standard diving equipment.

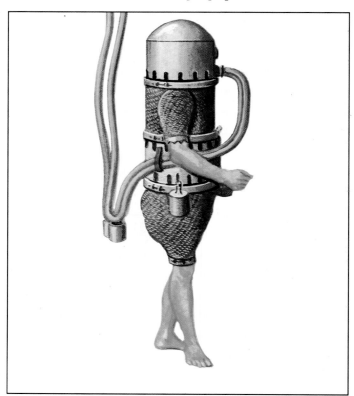

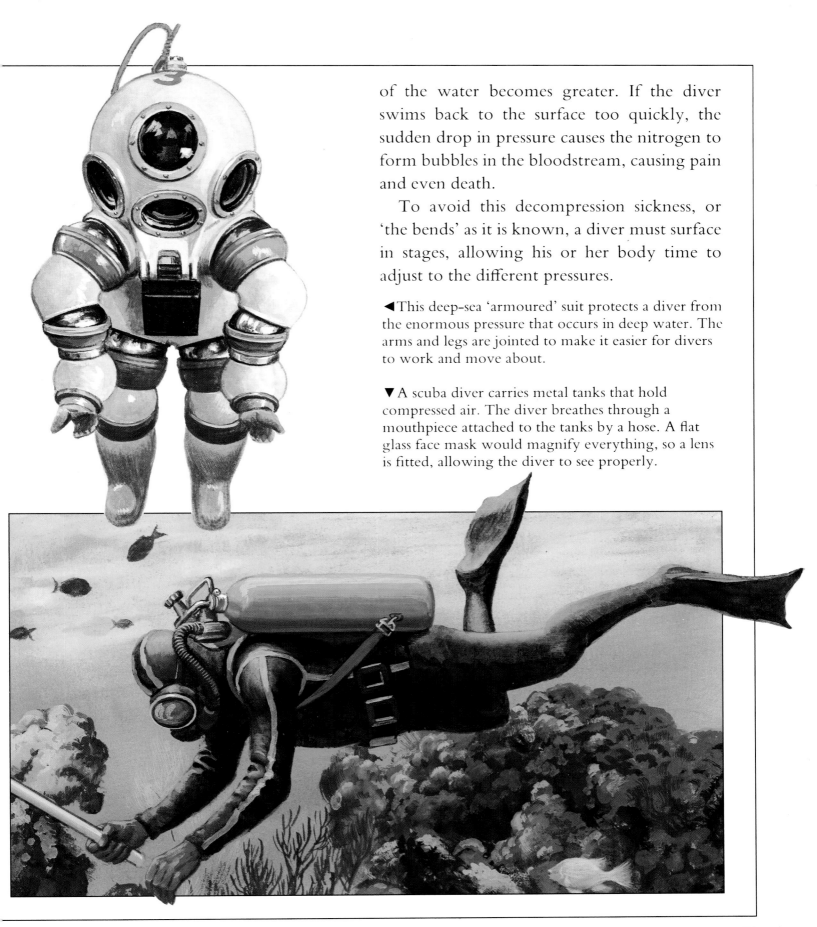

of the water becomes greater. If the diver swims back to the surface too quickly, the sudden drop in pressure causes the nitrogen to form bubbles in the bloodstream, causing pain and even death.

To avoid this decompression sickness, or 'the bends' as it is known, a diver must surface in stages, allowing his or her body time to adjust to the different pressures.

◄This deep-sea 'armoured' suit protects a diver from the enormous pressure that occurs in deep water. The arms and legs are jointed to make it easier for divers to work and move about.

▼A scuba diver carries metal tanks that hold compressed air. The diver breathes through a mouthpiece attached to the tanks by a hose. A flat glass face mask would magnify everything, so a lens is fitted, allowing the diver to see properly.

Exploring the Depths

The Earth's vast oceans contain a rich and varied world which, until recently, was largely unknown and unexplored.

There were many early attempts to devise machines and equipment that would allow people to explore the ocean depths, but it was only in the 1900s that undersea exploration really took off. By this time, the first practical submarines had arrived, and improvements in other diving equipment soon followed.

Today, various types of underwater craft called submersibles, protect people from the high pressure underwater and enable them to observe and work at greater depths than ever

▶ Depths in the ocean vary enormously. The continental shelf reaches a depth of about 180 metres. It then ends abruptly in a steep drop, known as the continental slope. This underwater cliff goes down about 3800 metres to the actual ocean floor.

This vast area covers about half of the Earth's surface and contains huge underwater mountains and deep cracks called trenches.

UNDERWATER EXPLORERS

(1) Deep-sea divers in armoured suits to protect them from the pressure breathe air that is supplied to them from the surface.

(2) FLIP is a ship that can turn itself on end by flooding special tanks. The submerged part carries research equipment.

(3) Divers use submersibles to check and repair underwater machinery used in ocean oilfields.

(4) The L-Class submersible is typical of this type. It is very manoeuvrable and can also be used for underwater rescue missions.

(5) Nuclear submarines stay submerged for months at a time.

(6) *Alvin* is a special deep-sea research vehicle.

(7) The bathyscaphe *Trieste*, the deepest diver of all.

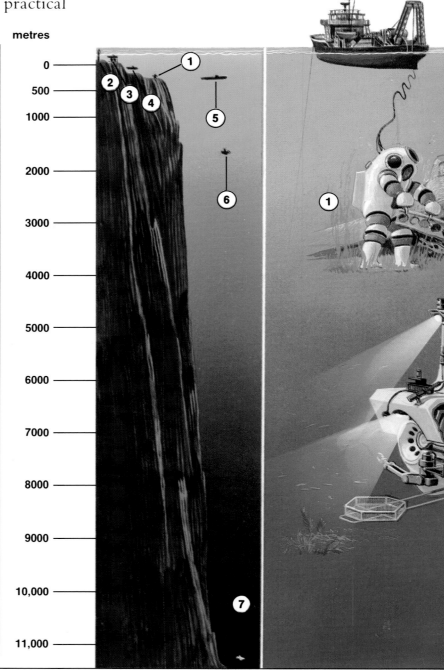

metres

0
500
1000
2000
3000
4000
5000
6000
7000
8000
9000
10,000
11,000

fore. Submersibles can travel down to 1200 metres, and stay there for up to 48 hours. They are capable of a wide range of tasks and can be fitted with cameras, underwater lights and mechanical arms to lift and carry objects about. In the future, new models will probably be able to dive to a depth of over 6000 metres.

In 1960, a specially designed submersible, called a bathyscaphe, descended to the bottom of the Marianas Trench in the Pacific Ocean. At 11,000 metres, this is the deepest known place in the world. Unlike other submersibles, however, a bathyscaphe can do little more than go up and down.

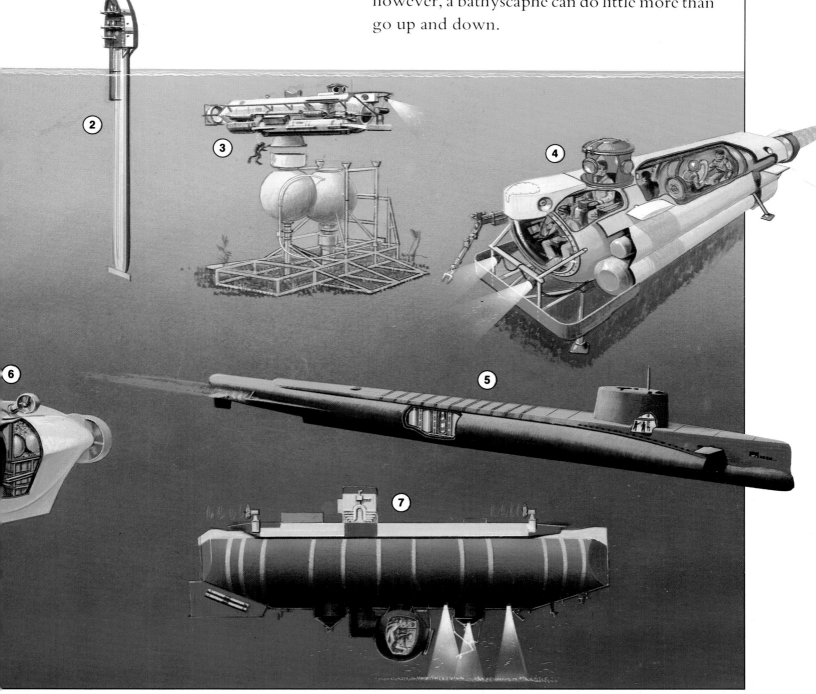

The Japanese were the first to farm both seaweed and pearls. The seaweed fields are rows of stakes, which are driven into the seabed in shallow coastal waters. The stakes provide a surface for the seaweed to cling to. When the seaweed is harvested it is used in a variety of foods, including ice cream.

Divers still collect natural pearls from oysters on the seabed, but in 1893 the Japanese successfully 'planted' and grew a pearl inside an oyster. Growing these 'cultured' pearls is now very profitable.

Underwater Farming

For thousands of years people have caught fish in the sea and the food supply in the oceans and seas seemed endless. In the past 50 years, however, fishing methods have changed and are now so efficient that many fish are becoming scarce.

Modern Fishing

Today, fishing fleets use sonar to find the really big shoals of fish. Powerful fishing boats, called trawlers, drag huge nets through the water, scooping up almost everything in their path.

Vast quantities of fish are caught every year, and in some cases this has led to overfishing, where certain species are being killed faster than they can breed.

The solution may be to farm fish instead of hunting them. Experiments in undersea farming are already being carried out in a number of different countries.

Raising Fish

The most efficient method of farming fish is to raise them from eggs in underwater enclosures. In the future, air pumps could be used to collect plankton from the sea, and pump it into the enclosures along with fishmeal to feed the fish. Farmers could supervise the fish from mini-submarines.

Larger fish might be kept in bubble pens. Walls of bubbles could be made to rise from air pipes on the seabed. Fish will not swim through such disturbed water. Helicopters could bring supplies and collect the fish to take them to market.

Nutritious Seaweed

A seaweed called giant kelp grows half a metre a day in the warm waters off California. It too may be farmed in the future, because it contains chemicals which could make it a useful source of food.

Wealth from the Sea

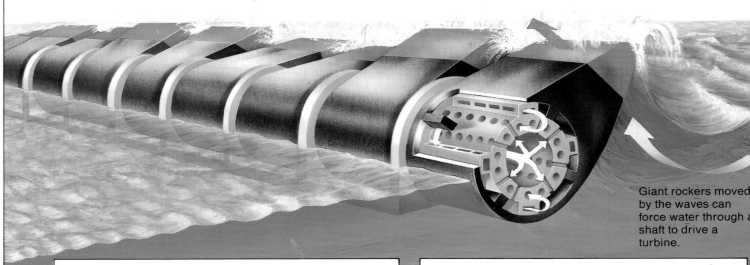

Giant rockers moved by the waves can force water through a shaft to drive a turbine.

We are only beginning to tap the vast wealth of the sea. The restless energy of the waves and tides could provide endless power supplies, and there are many rich mineral deposits beneath the sea.

Mining the Sea

More than a third of the world's oil comes from beneath the sea, but other minerals still wait to be extracted. Sulphur and manganese occur in huge amounts, washed into the sea by rivers or forced up from the Earth's interior by volcanic eruptions. Small nodules or lumps of manganese are scattered thickly over parts of the seabed. These nodules also contain the minerals copper, nickel and cobalt.

Water Power

In a tidal power station, the tidal flow is channelled through tunnels and used to drive the blades of turbine generators. The blades spin in either direction so that

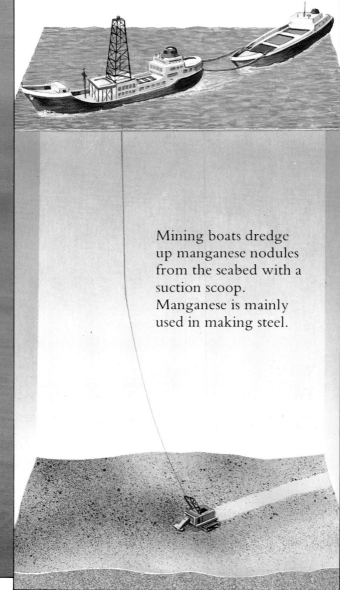

Mining boats dredge up manganese nodules from the seabed with a suction scoop. Manganese is mainly used in making steel.

Oil and other pollutants affect both ocean and seashore life.

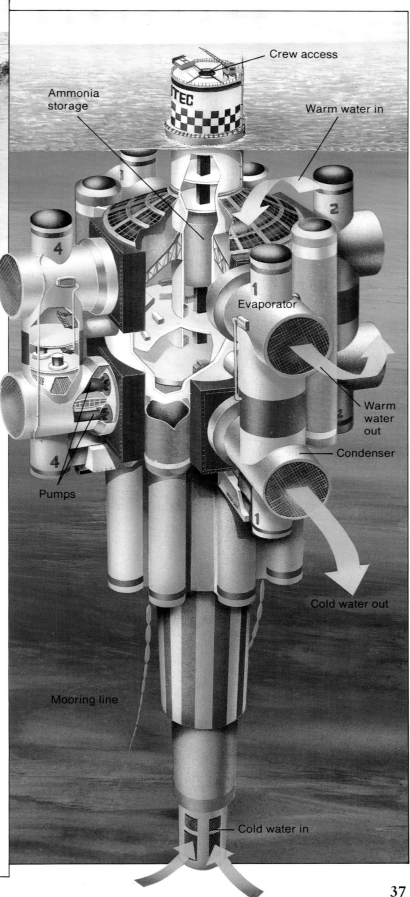

Crew access

Ammonia storage

Warm water in

Evaporator

Warm water out

Condenser

Cold water out

Pumps

Mooring line

Cold water in

power is generated as the tide both ebbs and flows. The tumbling motion of the waves can also be harnessed to make electricity (see above left).

In the floating thermal power station shown on the right, cold water taken from a depth of 450 metres is used in condensers to cool tanks of ammonia fluid. Warm surface water is pumped through the ammonia, which vaporizes into gas. The expanding gas drives an electricity generator. The ammonia is then condensed back to a fluid, and recycled as the process repeats itself.

Wasting our Wealth

To a world greedy for energy, the sea appears a tempting treasure house. But for too long, we have used the sea as a dustbin, fouling it with waste and other pollutants and destroying its delicately balanced patterns of life. We must take greater care of our seas if we are to benefit from their wealth.

New Technology

Oil is an important source of energy, and huge oilfields have been discovered beneath the seabed. But in order to reach the oil, engineers have to make use of a wide range of new underwater technology.

Drilling at Sea

Oil rigs at sea have to be strong enough to withstand waves and fierce winds, and yet still able to float. Around the wellhead, the place where the oil comes out from the seabed, divers must continually check and repair the pumping equipment and the many pipelines and storage tanks.

Small electric-powered submersibles with remote-control arms do most of the heavy work at depth. Robot tractors lay pipelines, guided by the submersible's crew.

On the Seabed

In the future, seabed oilfields could soon be built like the one shown here. Oil drilling and pumping could be carried out on the seabed. In this way, the storms and huge waves, which are the major problem for surface oil rigs, would be avoided.

Pumping stations would be reached by special watertight doors, called air locks. The divers could then take off their aqualungs and work in comfort. The oil could be stored in huge underwater tanks and pumped up to tankers on the surface, as needed. Large freight submarines could carry supplies and crew members between the shore and the under-water oilfields.

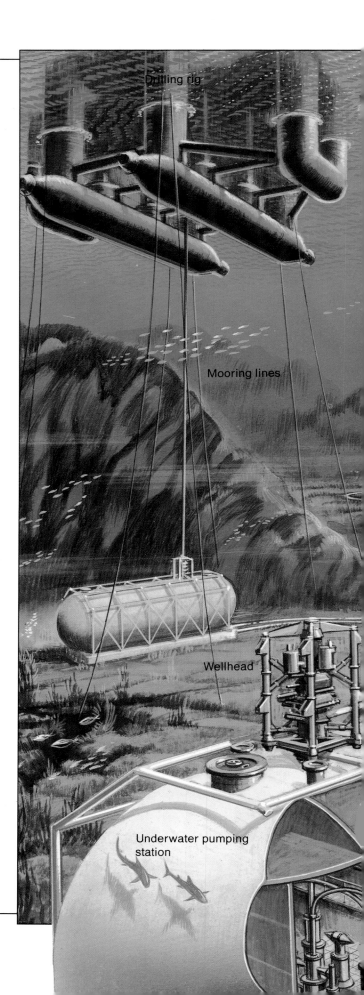

Drilling rig

Mooring lines

Wellhead

Underwater pumping station

Oil storage tanks

Tanker

Supply submarine

Oil storage tanks

Submersible

Entrance hatch

Living Under the Sea

Living beneath the sea has some similar problems to living in Space – lack of air and the way different pressures affect our bodies. Unlike Space, however, the sea does contain oxygen which, one day, we might be able to breathe directly from the water.

Living in a Laboratory

Scientists have studied these problems while living inside special underwater laboratories. In one such laboratory, called *Sealab III*, divers breathed a mixture of oxygen and helium instead of the oxygen and nitrogen that we normally breathe. This mixture reduces the chance of suffering from decompression sickness, or the bends.

Different teams of divers each spent periods of up to 12 days living in *Sealab III*. Both before and after their stay in

An underwater city of the future

In the future, cities could be built at sea. The thick outer wall would contain housing and create a protected water area inside.

the Sealab, the divers had to spend time in a decompression chamber. This is like a room in which pressure can be changed, to allow divers to get used to the difference.

In the Future

There is plenty of oxygen in sea water. Fish get the oxygen they need by 'breathing' through their gills. These are special organs that filter oxygen from the water, as our lungs filter oxygen from the air.

In theory, people could live underwater by breathing through artificial materials, called polymers, which would keep water out but let the oxygen in. If this is so, undersea cities could be built, like the one shown opposite, where people could live and work. However, polymers are still very experimental, so for the time being divers have to rely on their scuba gear whenever they move outside the safety of their seabed bases.

Submarines

Right from the start submarines were seen as secret underwater attack craft, against which even the mightiest navy would be helpless. And it was this idea that gave rise to their invention and development.

The First Submarines

In the 1600s, Dutch and French engineers devised primitive submarines worked by oars or paddles, but they weren't very effective and little use was made of them.

However, during the war between North America and Britain, from 1775 to 1783, the Americans needed an underwater weapon to attack the powerful British navy that was blockading their ports.

A young American called David Bushnell designed a small hand-powered submarine, the *Turtle*, which was intended to attack British ships by screwing mines into their wooden hulls. The plan failed, but the idea of using underwater weapons remained.

More experimental submarines were built during the 1800s, to the amusement of most ship designers, who never thought that they would work. Most were steam-driven and could not dive very deep or for very long.

The first successful seagoing submarine, the USS *Holland* of 1897, used electric motors when submerged and diesel engines for surface cruising. USS *Holland* proved that submarines could be used effectively after all.

NUCLEAR SUBMARINES

Like other submarines, nuclear submarines use periscopes and radar to identify ships on the surface. Below water, they use sonar to find and track their targets.

Nuclear submarines are almost impossible to detect. They can stay submerged for very long periods. With a generator and distiller they can use sea water to make oxygen for breathing and fresh water to drink. Some of their missiles have a long range and are very accurate. Today, the most powerful ships in the world sail beneath, and not on, the sea.

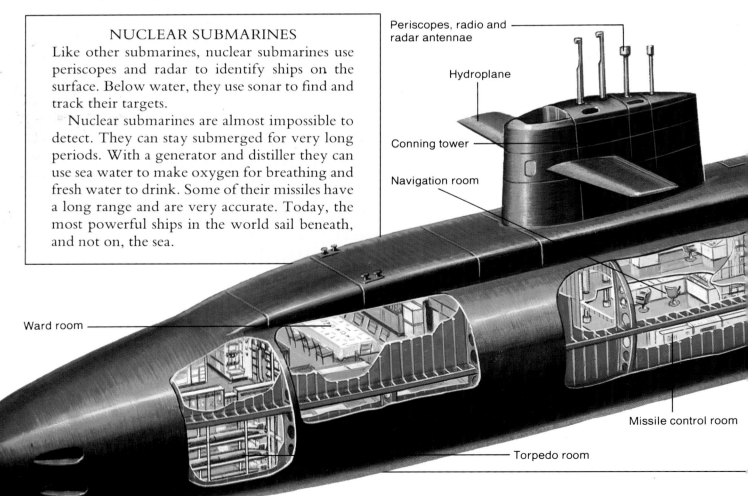

Periscopes, radio and radar antennae

Hydroplane

Conning tower

Navigation room

Ward room

Missile control room

Torpedo room

Submarines in War

In both World Wars, the submarine proved a deadly enemy to ships. Armed with explosive torpedoes, they would hide beneath the water, lying in wait for convoys of ships to pass.

Today, modern submarines are even more deadly. Many are powered by small nuclear reactors, and can can remain underwater for months at a time – the record is 111 days! They carry long-range missiles with nuclear warheads, which can travel thousands of kilometres to their target, as well as torpedoes and short-range missiles.

David Bushnell's *Turtle* was an early type of submarine. It had a pump system to make it dive and surface. The sailor pedalled a propeller, in the shape of a large screw.

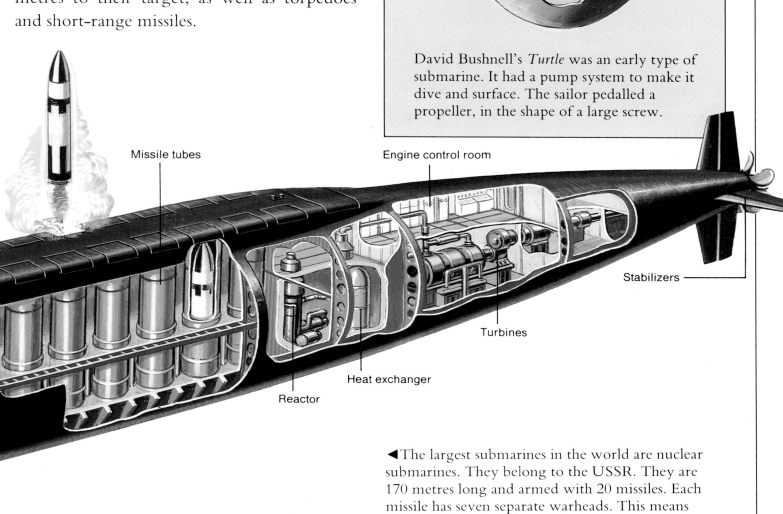

Missile tubes

Engine control room

Stabilizers

Turbines

Heat exchanger

Reactor

◄The largest submarines in the world are nuclear submarines. They belong to the USSR. They are 170 metres long and armed with 20 missiles. Each missile has seven separate warheads. This means that each submarine has 140 warheads capable of creating huge nuclear explosions.

Monsters and Mysteries

Sailors' stories from the past are full of strange, sometimes magical, monsters. But do any of them really exist?

The Sea Serpent and the Kraken

Certainly no sea snake is large enough to be mistaken for the mythical sea serpent. But the strange-looking oarfish, shown below, is the right shape and grows to a length of 10 metres.

The kraken is another popular myth and is often described as looking like a

The kraken was believed to live off the coast of Scandinavia. Its writhing arms were said to drag ships down into the deep.

THE UNICORN OF THE SEA

The narwhal (below) is the sea's answer to the legend of the unicorn. The narwhal is a small Arctic whale and the male has a long, twisted horn growing out of its upper jaw. In fact, the 'horn' is a tooth, which can grow to a length of 3 metres. Since the narwhal eats fish and squid, which it swallows whole, it is unlikely that its horn is used for hunting – in fact, the purpose of its curious horn is still unknown.

giant squid. The largest squids live in very deep waters, but occasionally appear on the surface. Their tentacle arms may be up to 15 metres long.

Mermaid or Manatee?

Everyone knows that the mermaid is supposed to be a beautiful woman, with long hair and a fish's tail. But it seems that the manatee, a plant-eating mammal, is the sea's only answer to the legend of the beautiful mermaids.

The manatee is the most likely source of the mermaid legend. The females nurse their young while floating upright in the water and, from a distance, could look like mermaids.

Sunken Treasure

The seabed is a graveyard of sunken ships. These hidden wrecks sometimes contain treasures that are not only valuable, but also tell us about the past.

Diving for Gold

Ships known to contain valuable cargoes cause the most excitement. The British warship *Association* sank off the Scilly Isles in 1707. Its cargo of gold was recovered by divers in the 1960s.

Learning About the Past

However, other finds are equally as valuable to archaeologists. Pottery is often very well preserved, and whole cargoes of wine jars have been recovered from wrecked Greek sailing ships. Cannon and anchors also survive, but being made of iron often rust.

All underwater treasure must be treated very carefully when it is taken up to the surface, or it could simply crumble into dust. A sunken ship is a delicate time capsule, giving us a glimpse of how life was lived long ago.

Useful Words

Algae A group of simple non-flowering plants, most of which live in water. Some algae are minute and consist of just one cell. Others, such as seaweed, are larger and contain many cells.

Atmosphere The air that surrounds the Earth. Air is made up of many different gases, but nitrogen and oxygen are the commonest gases.

Bathyscaphe An underwater craft that is capable of withstanding the enormous pressure in the deepest parts of the ocean. Bathyscaphes are used for all kinds of scientific experiments and for exploration.

Cell The smallest unit of life, from which all plants and animals are made. A few plants and animals consist of only one cell, but most are made up of millions of cells.

Compressed air Air in which the gases have been tightly pressed together inside a container.

Continental shelf An underwater rocky ledge which surrounds most of the Earth's continents.

Continental slope An underwater cliff which stretches from the continental shelf down to the ocean floor.

Decompression chamber A sealed room inside which the pressure can be slowly increased or decreased to allow a diver's body to adjust to the required level of pressure.

Equator An imaginary circle drawn around the middle of the Earth, half way between the North Pole and the South Pole.

Estuary The area of water where a river reaches the sea. It is sometimes called the mouth of the river.

Gill The breathing mechanism inside the body of many animals that live in water. A gill is like a very fine mesh which can extract oxygen from water and pass it into the bloodstream.

Gravity The invisible force that pulls everything towards the centre of the Earth or towards any other large object, such as the Sun or the Moon. The larger the object, the greater the force of gravity.

Larva (plural **larvae**) The young form of some kinds of animal – for example, some insects and fish – when they hatch from their eggs.

Mammal An animal that gives birth to live young and feeds them with milk from its own body. Mammals are warm-blooded and usually have hair or fur on their bodies.

Migration A long journey made at a regular time of year by an animal, usually in search of food or breeding grounds.

Photosynthesis The process by which most plants make food using sunlight, air and water.

Phytoplankton Plant plankton.

Plankton A name used to describe hundreds of different tiny plants and animals that drift in the surface waters of the sea and provide food for thousands of other sea creatures.

Predator An animal that hunts other animals for food.

Spawn The soft, sometimes jelly-like eggs of creatures that breed in water.

Tide The rise and fall of the sea that takes place twice in every 24 hours. Tides are caused by the pull of the Moon's gravity.

Vertebrate An animal that has a backbone. Fish, amphibians and mammals are vertebrates.

Water pressure The weight of water pressing down from above. Water pressure increases with depth.

Zooplankton Animal plankton.

Index

A
albacore 24
Alvin submarine 32–33
angler fish 20–21
aqualungs 30–31, 38
archer fish 14
Atlantic Ocean 6, 27
Australian seahorses 23

B
barracudas 10
bathyscaphes 32–33, 47
beluga whales 19
bends, the 31, 40
blue whales 18–19
breathing underwater
    30–31, 40–41
breeding 26–27
Bushnell, David 42–43

C
catfish 13
clams 28–29
cleaner fish 10
cockles 14, 15
continental shelf 6, 32,
    47
continental slope 32, 47
coral reefs 16–17
crabs 14–15
crayfish 26
crown of thorns starfish
    16, 17
currents 8–9
cuttlefish 15

D
damsel fish 23
decompression, sickness
    31, 40;
    chamber 41, 47
decoy fish 24
deep-sea fish 20–21
diving 30–31, 32, 38, 41
dolphins 18–19

E
eels 26–27, 28–29
elvers 27

F
false cleaners 10
fiddler crabs 14
fish, eye 12;
    movement 12
fishing 35
FLIP 32–33
flying fish 24

G
gills 41, 47
goby 12
grey whales 18
groupers 16–17

H
hagfish 22–23
Halley's diving bell 30
hammerhead sharks 28
Holland, USS 42

I
icebergs, 6–7
iguanas, marine 22

J
jellyfish 28–29

K
kelp 35
killer whales 18–19
Klingert diving suit 30
kraken 44–45
krill 18

L
larvae 27, 47
lateral line organ 13
leptocephali 27
limpets 15
lugworms 14

M
mammals 18–19, 47
manatees 45
manta rays 22
Marianas Trench 33
mermaids 45
migration 26–27, 47

minerals 36
missiles 42–43
moray eels 28–29
mudskippers 15

N
narwhals 44
nuclear submarines
    32–33, 42–43

O
oarfish 44
ocean currents 8–9
ocean floor 6, 32
oil 36–37, 38–39
oxygen 40, 41
oysters 34

P
Pacific Ocean 6, 26, 33
parrot fish 16–17
pearls 30, 34
periwinkles 15
phytoplankton 11, 47
piddocks 14
pilot fish 25
plaice 13
plankton 11, 16, 18, 35,
    47
Plimsoll line 6
pollution 37
polyps 16
porcupine fish 25
porpoises 18
Portuguese men-of-war
    28–29

R
rays 22
razor shells 14–15

S
salmon 26
sand eels 15
Sargasso Sea 27
scorpion fish 28–29
scuba diving 30–31, 41
sea anemones 17, 23
seabed 6–7

sea cucumbers 14
sea dragons 23
sea mice 15
sea serpents 44
sea slugs 14, 22–23
sea spiders 23
sea urchins 29
Sealab III 40–41
seals 11, 26–27
seaweed 15, 34–35
sharks 19, 25, 28–29
shellfish 11, 15
shipwrecks 46
skate 14
snakes 23, 44
sperm whales 18, 24–25
squid 11, 20, 25, 44–45
squirrel fish 16–17
starfish 14, 16–17, 25
submarines 32–33, 35,
    38–39, 42–43
submersibles 32–33, 38
sunfish 12
swim bladders 12

T
tides 8, 47
tidal power 36–37
trenches, oceanic 6, 32
Trieste bathyscaphe
    32–33
trigger fish 24
Turtle submarine 42–43

U
unicorns 44

V
verterbrate 12, 47

W
water power 36–37
waves 8
weapons 42, 43
whales 11, 18–19, 44
wrecks 46

Z
zooplankton 11, 47